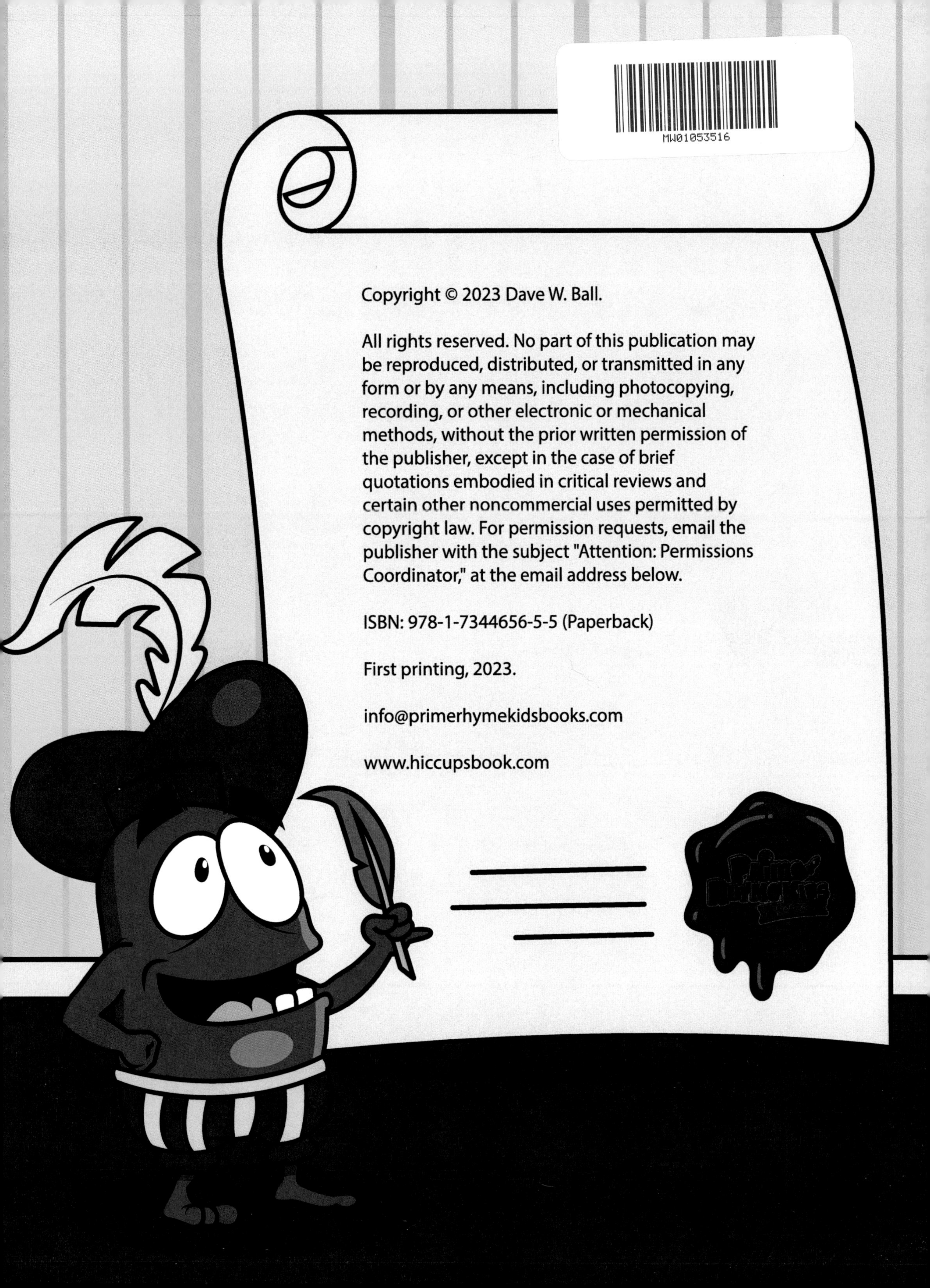

ISBN: 978-1-7344656-5-5 (Paperback)

First printing, 2023.

info@primerhymekidsbooks.com

www.hiccupsbook.com

WRITTEN BY DAVE W. BALL
ILLUSTRATED BY DESIGN PICKLE

In the moonlit night, what a fright!
Count Hiccup pops out, filled with delight.
Can you find these 4 eerie items?
5 Purple Skulls
4 Spiders
3 Witch Hats
4 Candles

In a brown pot, the witch stirs with might,
A special potion, brewing magic through the night.
Can you find these 4 magical items?
5 Mushrooms
3 Bats
3 Witch Broomsticks
3 Jack O'Lanterns

Green skulls and jack o'lanterns light up the scene,
A Hiccup as a mummy, a funny Halloween!
Can you find these 4 spooky items?
4 Jack O'Lanterns
3 Green Skulls
3 Witch Hats
5 Candies

Hiccup the witch, with hat and broom,
Flying through the night with a magical zoom.
Can you find these 4 witchy items?
2 Witches
3 Broomsticks
4 Ghosts
1 Moon

In the bubbling cauldron, together they play,
Stirring up mischief on this Halloween day!
Can you find these 4 haunting items?
3 Spiders
4 Voodoo Dolls
2 Spider Webs
3 Bats

RIP
RIP
RIP
Hiccup the vampire, in the graveyard he stands,
Tombstones and ghosts, eerie sights in these lands.
Can you find these 4 eerie items?
RIP
4 Jack O'Lanterns
3 Ghosts
3 Tombstones
1 Bat

RIP
RIP
RIP
Hiccup as Jason, a chilling sight to see,
In the graveyard, where shadows creep with glee.
Can you find these 4 frightening items?
RIP
4 Crows
3 Scarecrows
3 Tombstones
4 Reaper Scythes

Hiccup the witch, stirs the green potion's brew,
With spiders, broomsticks, candles, and a black cat too.
Can you find these 4 scary items?
1 Cat
2 Broomsticks
3 Candles
2 Spiders

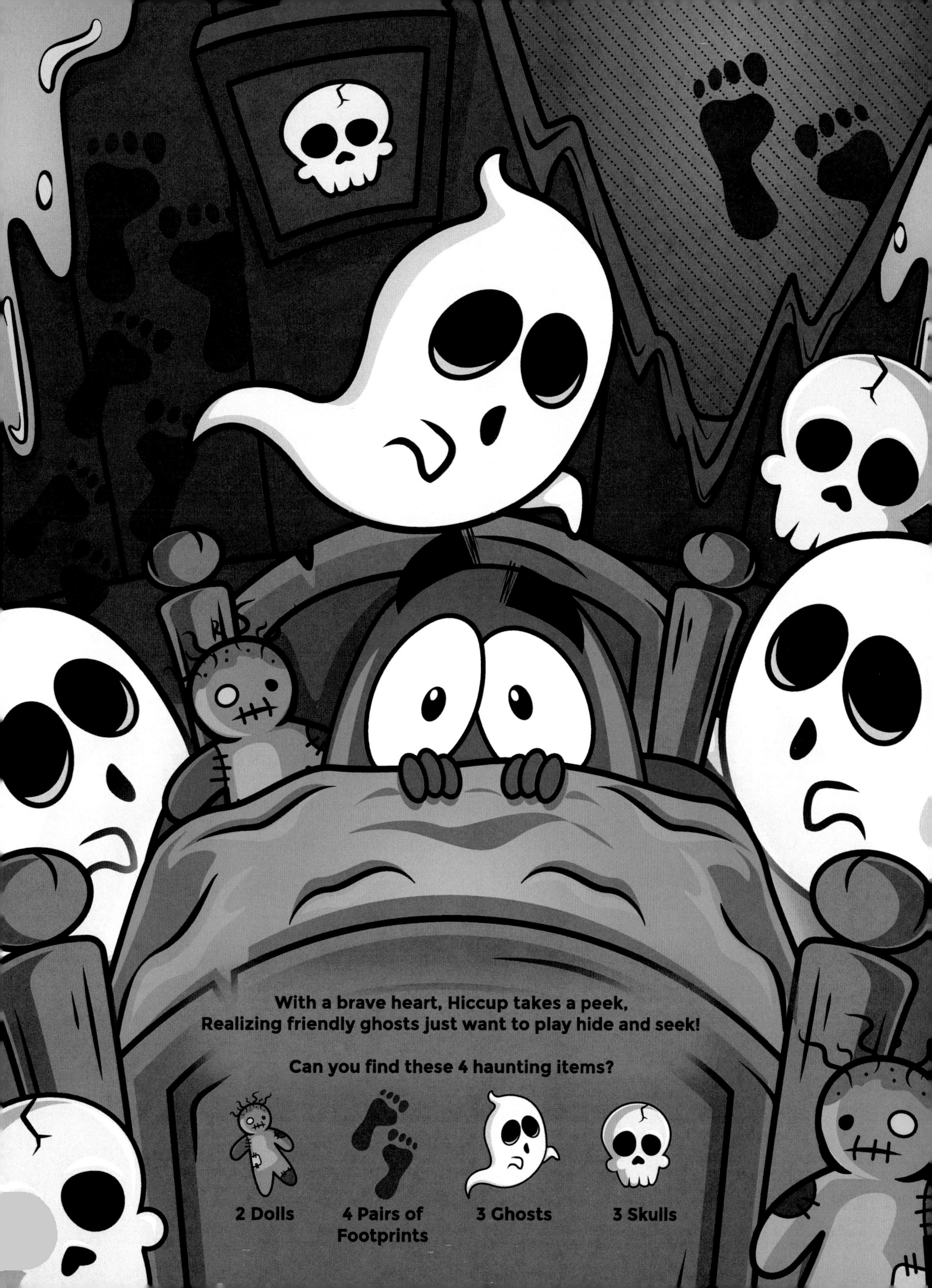
With a brave heart, Hiccup takes a peek,
Realizing friendly ghosts just want to play hide and seek!
Can you find these 4 haunting items?
2 Dolls
4 Pairs of Footprints
3 Ghosts
3 Skulls

In the lab, Hiccup, a friendly Frankenstein,
With test tubes and remotes, experimenting all the time.
Can you find these 4 creepy items?
5 Eyeballs
2 Brains
7 Test Tubes
2 Remotes

From the coffin, wrapped in linen so tight,
Hiccup emerges, bringing ancient delight.
Can you find these 4 mystical items?
7 Torches
3 Sphynx Cats
5 Vases
6 Eye of Horus

RIP
With scythe in hand, Hiccup walks the night,
A haunting figure, casting an eerie delight.
Can you find these 4 ghostly items?
5 Skulls
3 Scythes
4 Ghosts
3 Owls

RIP
Surrounded by wolves, a pack at their side,
Hiccup howls with delight, joining the wild tide.
Can you find these 4 spooky items?
3 Gas Lamps
4 Axes
6 Yellow Bones
4 Wolves

Hiccup the pirate, sailing with glee,
A steering wheel of bones guides the sea.
Can you find these 4 cursed items?
3 Scrolls
3 Pipes
4 Pirate Hats
4 Telescopes

Hiccup wears a mask, a hockey fright,
With a golf club in hand, ready to strike.
Can you find these 4 frightening items?
3 Bear Traps
5 Golf Clubs
3 Potions
4 Octopus Telescopes

Hiccup the scarecrow, in fields so wide,
Holds a rake, standing tall with pride.
Can you find these 4 sinister items?
3 Bales of Hay
4 Straw Hats
3 Scarecrows
4 Rakes

RIP
RIP
RIP
RIP
Ghosts and ghouls, they do arise,
A Hiccups haunted house, full of surprise.
Can you find these 4 haunted items?
RIP
1 Spider
3 Hiccups
3 Trick-or-Treat Buckets
4 Tombstones

RIP
RIP
RIP
RIP
RIP
RIP
Amongst the spirits, Hiccup finds delight,
A Halloween eve, shrouded in the night.
Can you find these 4 ominous items?
RIP
4 Dwarves
5 Black Cats
3 Grim Reapers
6 Tombstones

Hiccup the explorer, seeking treasures untold,
With a magnifyng glass, he's brave and bold.
Can you find these 4 adventure items?
3 Magnifying Glasses
5 Diamonds
3 Mummies
4 Gold Bars

MILK
MILK
MILK
Bones all around, but don't be scared,
Hiccup is a friendly skeleton, with fun to share.
Can you find these 4 mysterious items?
MILK
1 Orange Coffin
3 Milk Boxes
4 Red Candles
5 Purple Worms

Your voice truly matters. So if you enjoyed this book, it would mean the world to me if you would take a short minute to leave a heartfelt review on Amazon. Your kind feedback is very appreciated and so very important.
Thank you so much for your time!
HICCUP'S Haunted Halloween Hunt

TURN HICCUPS INTO SMILES
ADD MORE JOY TO YOUR BOOKSHELF
More Hiccups Books To Love
Hiccups
by David W. Ball
HICCUPS... AGAIN?
ABCs OF AFFIRMATION
Starring the Hiccups
Positive Affirmations For Toddlers
WILD THE HICCUPS WATERSLIDE RACE
DAVE W. BALL
More Hidden Picture
Books To Explore
HICCUPS AGAIN? EPIC ADVENTURE
FIND IT BOOK
HICCUP'S Haunted Halloween Hunt
An Epic Seek & Find It Book For Ages 3 - 5
Written By Dave W. Ball
Illustrated By Design Pickle
HICCUP'S HOLIDAY HUNT: A CHRISTMAS ADVENTURE
A Very Merry Look & Find Book For Ages 3 - 5
COMING SOON
HiccupsBook.com

Made in the USA
Las Vegas, NV
30 September 2023

78343008R00017